Contents — Viola Book Two

Boil 'em cabbage down

American

Boil 'em cab - bage down, down, Bake 'em bis - cuits brown, brown,

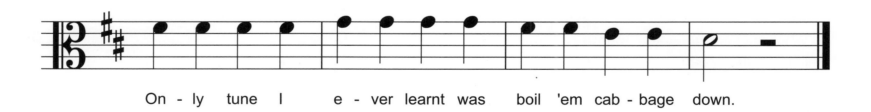

On - ly tune I e - ver learnt was boil 'em cab - bage down.

Happy days

Now the day is over

S Baring-Gould

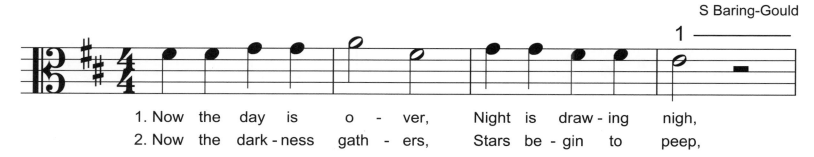

1. Now the day is o - ver, Night is draw - ing nigh,
2. Now the dark - ness gath - ers, Stars be - gin to peep,

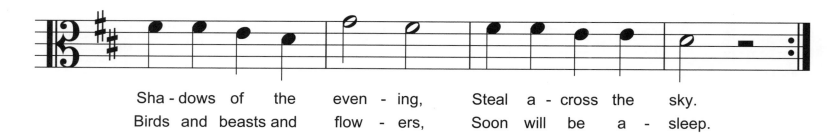

Sha - dows of the even - ing, Steal a - cross the sky.
Birds and beasts and flow - ers, Soon will be a - sleep.

Slurs join notes together in the same bow.

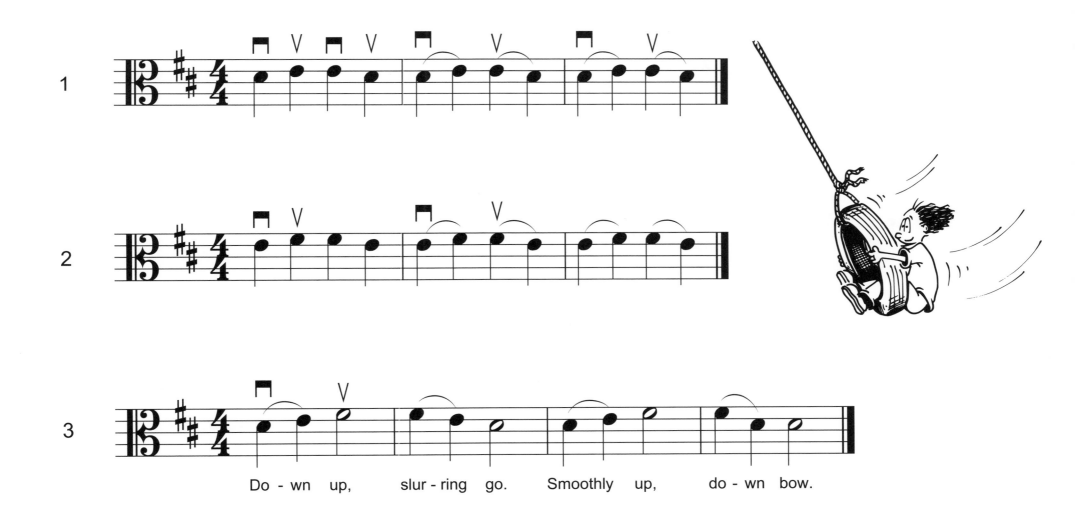

Do - wn up, slur - ring go. Smoothly up, do - wn bow.

Merry dance

16C French

Lucy Locket

Lu - cy Lock - et   lost her pock - et,   Kit - ty Fish - er   found   it,

Not a pen - ny   was there in it,   on - ly rib - bon   round it.

Bell song

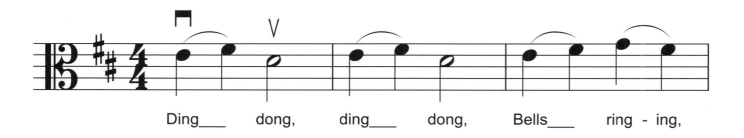

Ding___ dong, ding___ dong, Bells___ ring - ing,

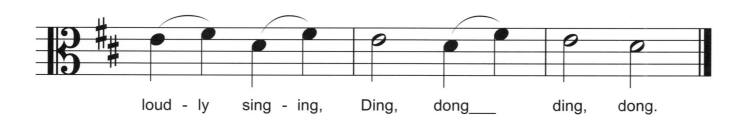

loud - ly sing - ing, Ding, dong___ ding, dong.

Frère Jacques

French round

Frè - re Jac - ques, Frè - re Jac - ques,

Dorm - ez vous? dorm - ez vous?

Son-nez les ma - ti - nes, son-nez les ma - ti - nes,

Din, din, don, din, din, don.

Frère Jacques

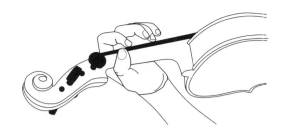

Cobbler, cobbler

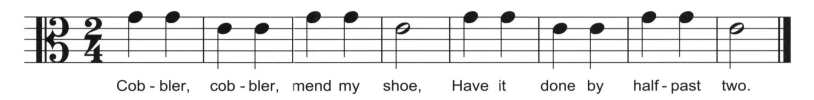

Cob - bler, cob - bler, mend my shoe, Have it done by half - past two.

Rain, rain, go away

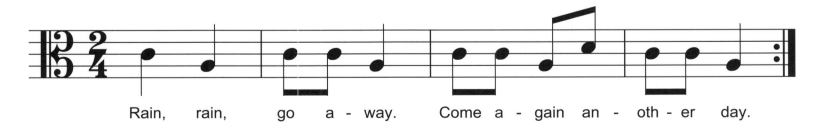

Rain, rain, go a - way. Come a - gain an - oth - er day.

Baa, baa, black sheep

Baa, baa, black sheep, have you a - ny wool?

Yes sir, yes sir, three bags full.

One for the mas - ter and one for the dame and

one for the lit - tle boy who lives down the lane.

Clock canon

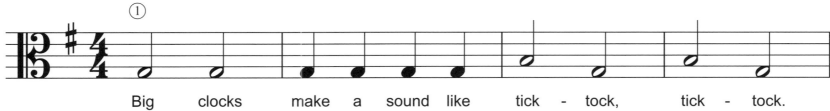

Big clocks make a sound like tick - tock, tick - tock.

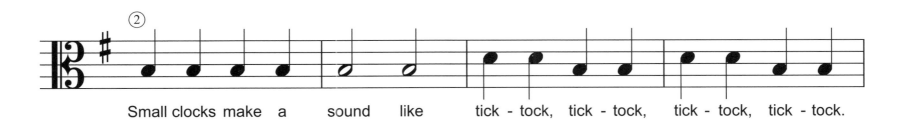

Small clocks make a sound like tick - tock, tick - tock, tick - tock, tick - tock.

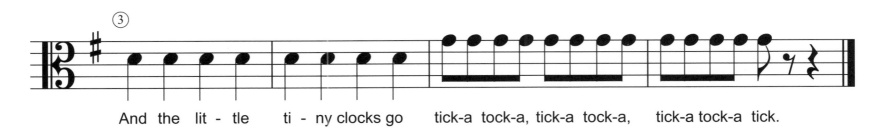

And the lit - tle ti - ny clocks go tick-a tock-a, tick-a tock-a, tick-a tock-a tick.

Dinah

American

No one in the house but Di - nah, Di - nah, No one in the house but me I know.

No one in the house but Di - nah, Di - nah, Play-ing on the old ban - jo.

Sailing on the ocean

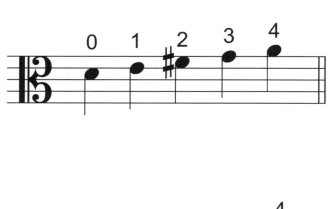

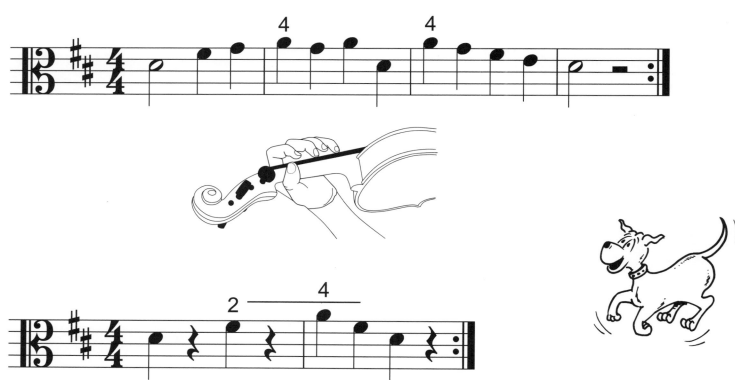

Love,   me,   love my dog.

Folk dance

French

$\boldsymbol{f}$ *(forte)* = loudly $\boldsymbol{p}$ *(piano)* = softly

Evening song

17C French

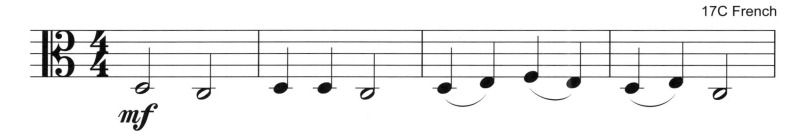

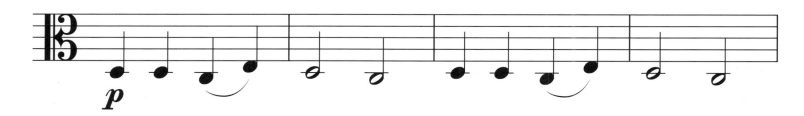

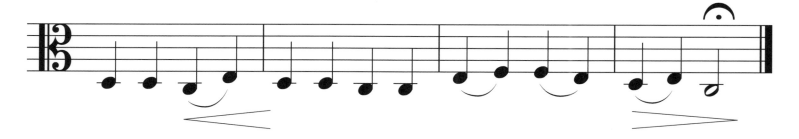

18

Listen!

French

cresc.

f

dim.

cresc. (*crescendo*) = gradually louder   *dim.* (*diminuendo*) = gradually softer

Keep 2 down.

Lis - ten to the cuck - oo,   cuck - oo,   cuck - oo,   cuck - oo.

20

There is a happy land

Add your own dynamics.

American Indian

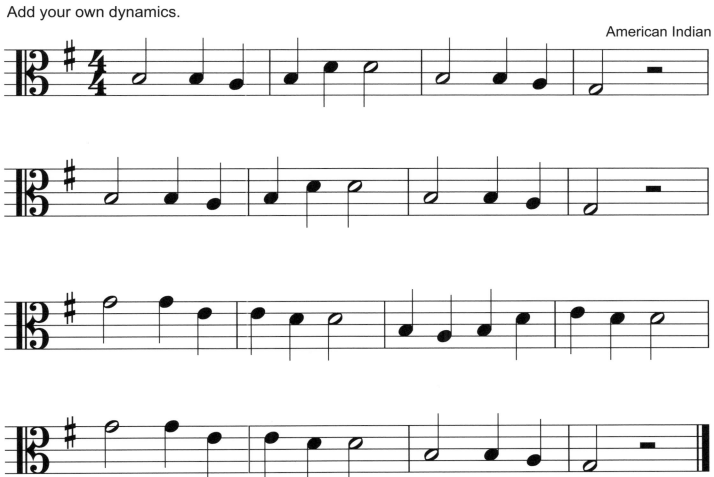

21

Blue bells, cockle shells

Blue bells   cock-le shells,   e - v - i - vy   o - ver.

Blue bells,   cock-le shells,   e - v - i - vy   o - ver.

This old man

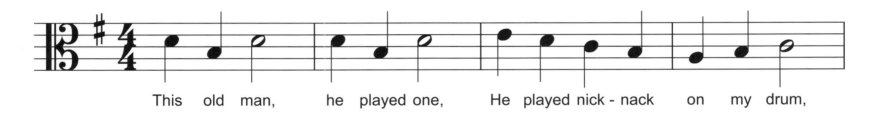

This old man, he played one, He played nick - nack on my drum,

nick - nack, paddy whack, give a dog a bone, This old man came roll - ing home.

Feel the beat

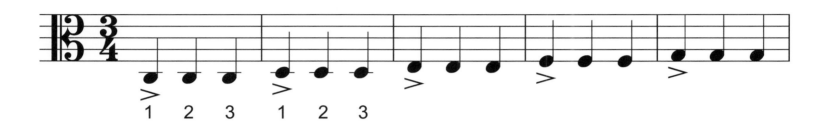

Bell horses

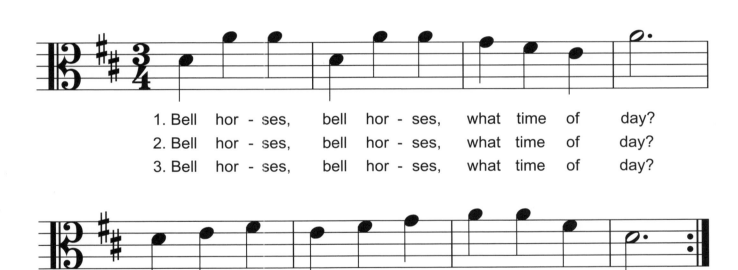

1. Bell hor - ses, bell hor - ses, what time of day?
2. Bell hor - ses, bell hor - ses, what time of day?
3. Bell hor - ses, bell hor - ses, what time of day?

One o' - clock, two o' - clock, three and a - way.
Two o' - clock, three o' - clock, four and a - way.
Five o' - clock, six o' - clock, now time to stay.

Two in the boat

American

Two in the boat and the tide rolls high,

Two in the boat and the tide rolls high,

Two in the boat and the tide rolls high,

Get you a pret - ty one, by and by.

French folk song

See saw sacradown

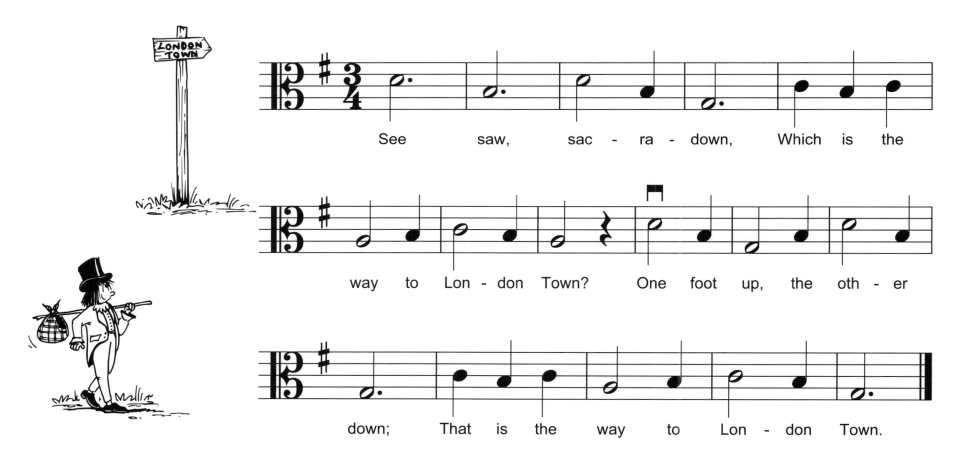

Polka

Scandinavian

Add your own dynamics.

My goose

Why shouldn't my goose, Sing as well as thy goose, When I paid for my goose, Twice as much as thou.

Round

Taffy

Taf-fy was a rob - ber,   Taf-fy was a thief.   Taf-fy came to my house and stole a leg of beef.

I came to Taf-fy's house, Taf-fy was in bed.   I took a marrow bone and hit him on the head! Biff!

Lightly row

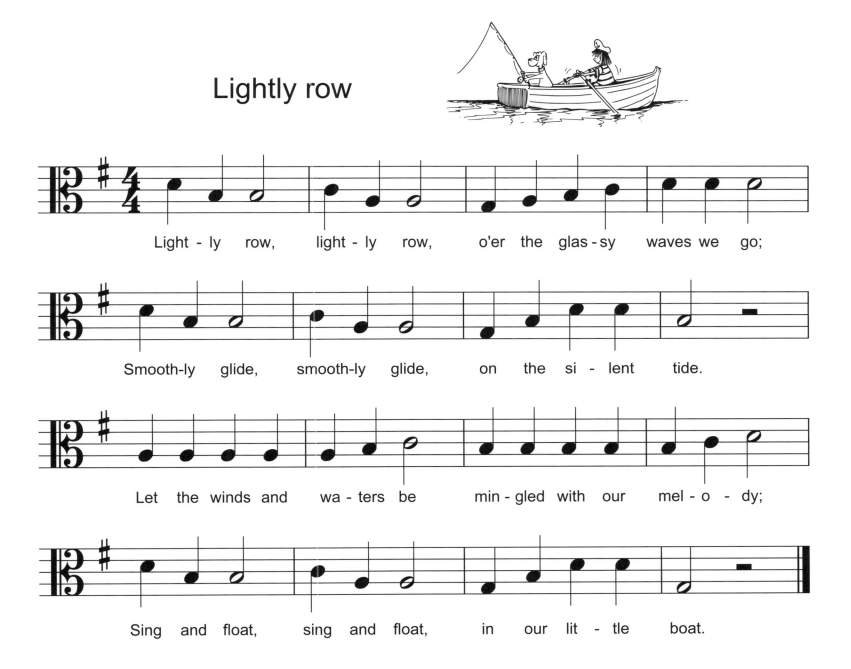

Light - ly row, light - ly row, o'er the glas - sy waves we go;

Smooth - ly glide, smooth - ly glide, on the si - lent tide.

Let the winds and wa - ters be min - gled with our mel - o - dy;

Sing and float, sing and float, in our lit - tle boat.

Jingle bells

J Pierpont

Jin - gle bells, jin - gle bells, jin - gle all the way,

Oh, what fun it is to ride in a one horse o - pen sleigh, Hey!

Jin - gle bells, jin - gle bells, jin - gle all the way,

Oh, what fun it is to ride in a one horse o - pen sleigh.

Merry dance

16C French

Bend backs

Rock-a-bye baby

mp Rock - a - bye, ba - by, on the tree top,

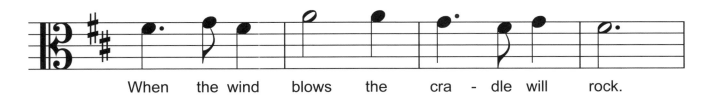

When the wind blows the cra - dle will rock.

When the bough breaks the cra - dle will fall,

Down will come ba - by, cra - dle, and all.

Au clair de la lune

French

Round

A Caldara
(1670-1736)

Canon

Hungarian

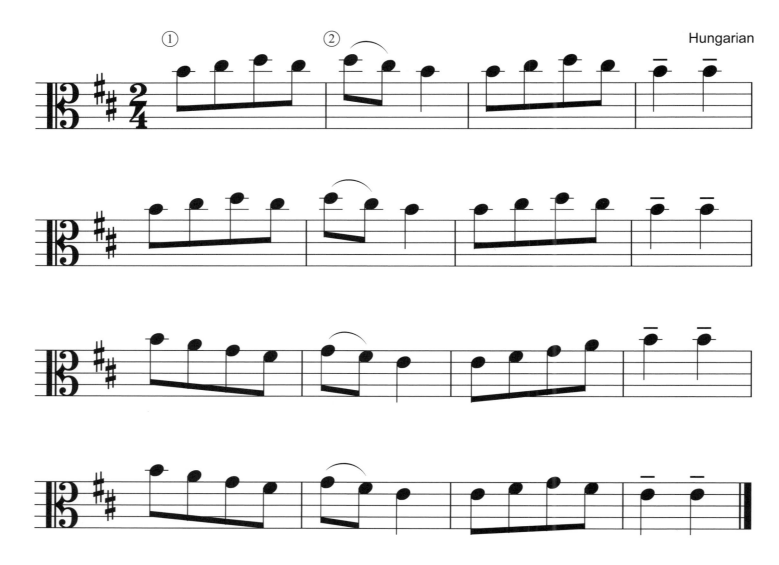

$\overline{\raisebox{0pt}{\rule{0pt}{6pt}}\!\bullet}$ = *tenuto* = play full value

Barcarolle

Jacques Offenbach

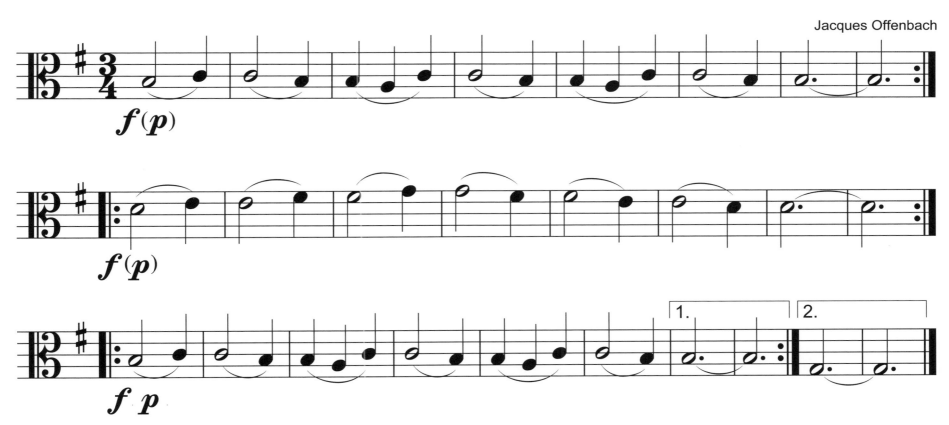

39

Donkey riding

Sea shanty

Were you ev - er in Que - bec, Stow - in' tim - ber on the deck,

Where there's a king with a gol - den crown, Rid - ing on a don - key?

Hey! Ho! A - way we go, Don - key rid - ing, don - key rid - ing,

Hey! ___ Ho! A - way we go, Rid - ing on a don - key!

Winds through the olive trees

Gascon carol

Winds through the o - live trees soft - ly did blow, a -

round lit - tle Beth - le - hem, lo - ng, long, a ____ - go.

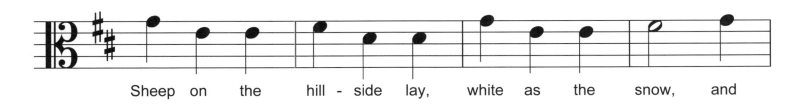

Sheep on the hill - side lay, white as the snow, and

shep - herds were watch - ing them, lo - ng, long, a ____ - go.

See-saw

Can-can

Offenbach

Leap frog

Scarborough Fair

English

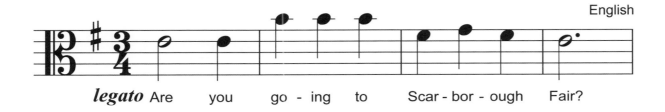

legato Are you go - ing to Scar - bor - ough Fair?

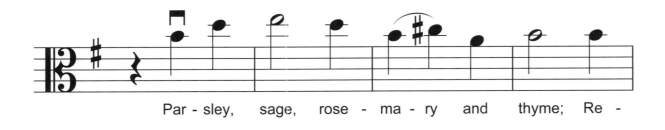

Par - sley, sage, rose - ma - ry and thyme; Re -

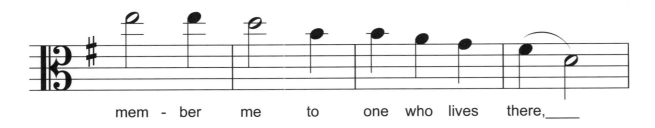

mem - ber me to one who lives there,____

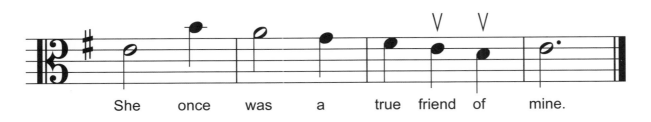

She once was a true friend of mine.

45

D major scale and arpeggio

G major scale and arpeggio

C major scale and arpeggio

Bowing variations (scale, arpeggio or melody)

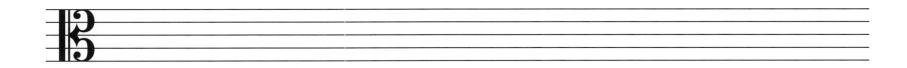

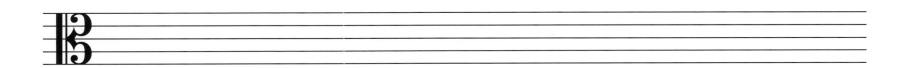

①

②

③

⑤

⑥

⑦

Name these signs and terms.

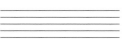　　alto clef

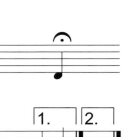

p = *piano* =

mp = *mezzo-piano* =

mf = *mezzo-forte* =

f = *forte* =

cresc. (*crescendo*) =

dim. (*diminuendo*) =

legato =

rit. (*ritenuto*) =

Fine =

D.C. al Fine =